בס״ד

לה״ו

This Book Belongs To:

Please Read It To Me!

A Little Girl Named Miriam

By Dina Rosenfeld

Drawings by Ilene Winn-Lederer

Hachai
PUBLISHING

בס"ד

In honor of my
"little girl named Miriam"
who also loves babies.
May her "outstanding qualities" and her love of
Jewish children continue to inspire as her namesake
Miriam bat Amram has done.
We will love and honor you always,
Dovid (and R.A.Y.A.) Gantshar

A Little Girl Named Miriam

To my father, Emil W. Herman z"l who was gentle, clever, courageous, and wise. D.L.R.

In Loving Memory to My Tante Miriam
And to Jeffrey, Joshua, Ira, and Malke Leah for the dreams we share. I.W.L.

First Edition — April 2001 / Nissan 5761
Copyright © 2001 by **Hachai Publishing**
ALL RIGHTS RESERVED

Layout: Eli Chaikin

LCCN: 00-107810
ISBN: 0-922613-79-6

Hachai Publishing
Brooklyn, N.Y.
Tel: 718-633-0100 - Fax: 718-633-0103
www.hachai.com - info@hachai.com

Printed in China

Glossary

Geulah	Redemption	**Mitzrayim**	Egypt
Hashem	G-d	**Moshe**	Moses
Midrash	Collected teaching of the sages	**Rabbeinu**	Our teacher
		Shabbos	Sabbath

*O*nce upon a time, in the land of Mitzrayim, there lived a little girl named Miriam who loved babies.

She loved their soft, silky hair, their scrunched-up faces and their tiny pink fingers. Whenever new babies were born, Miriam and her mother, Yocheved, always went to help.

First, Yocheved would make the babies look beautiful by washing them with warm water and gently smoothing their hair.

Then Miriam did her job. Holding a wiggly, crying baby close to her, she would make funny noises.

"Pu, pu, pu," she'd whisper over and over, "pu, pu, pu." Soon the baby would become calm and quiet, and fall asleep in Miriam's arms.

Miriam was *so good* at her job that everyone called her "Pu'ah," a name that sounded just like the gentle way she talked to babies.

One day, Pharaoh, the King of Mitzrayim, called for Miriam and Yocheved. The two of them walked into his palace and stood before his throne.

"I have decided," Pharaoh said in a big loud voice, "that you must stop taking care of newborn Jewish baby boys."

"What if one of them would grow up to be stronger than I am? He and all the Jewish people who work for me might leave Mitzrayim! Then who would carry heavy bricks for me and build my cities? I don't want there to be any more Jewish baby boys!"

That was the meanest thing Miriam had ever heard!
Even though Pharaoh was so strong, and she was just
a little girl, Miriam knew it was time to speak up.

"That is wicked," she said to Pharaoh.
"Hashem will never let your plan succeed!"
Everyone was amazed that little Pu'ah with the
soft voice could be so brave.

Of course, Miriam and her mother didn't listen to Pharaoh. They continued to take good care of all the babies — girls and boys.

But the Jewish people were worried when they heard that Pharaoh didn't want there to be any more baby boys. Miriam's father, Amram, and all the men were talking about what to do. Miriam and her younger brother, Aaron, listened quietly while their father spoke.

"I know what to do," Amram said.
"Let's not have any more babies at all.
Then Pharaoh won't be angry."

No more babies? Everyone looked sad, but they all agreed. Even though the grownups were so smart and she was only six years old, Miriam knew it was time to speak up.

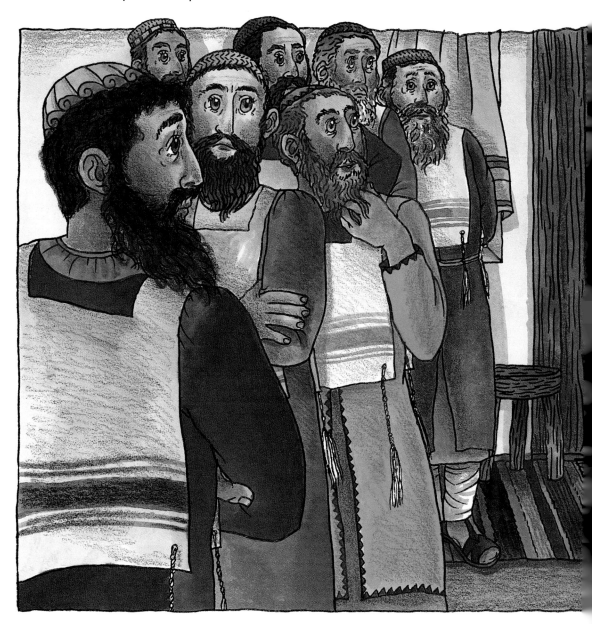

"Father," she said, "that idea would be even worse than Pharaoh's!"
Amram looked surprised, but he kept listening.

"Pharaoh said 'no more baby boys,' but this idea means there won't be any baby girls, either!" Everyone was amazed that little Miriam could be so wise.

"The child is right," said her father.
"We will continue to bring more babies into the world, and Hashem will help."

Miriam smiled. She just knew that
her parents would be the ones to
have the special baby boy that
Pharaoh was so worried about.
So Miriam spoke up again.

"You'll see," she said to her parents.
"You will have a son that will grow up
and lead all the Jews out of Mitzrayim!"

Yocheved and Amram were amazed that their
little girl could have such important ideas.
The whole family waited to see what would happen.
One fine Shabbos day in the springtime, Yocheved
had a baby, and sure enough, it was a boy!

When he was born, the whole house became filled
with a bright light that showed how special
he was.

Happily, Miriam's father kissed her right on the head. "My daughter," he said, "your words are coming true!"

Miriam and Aaron loved their new baby brother. But they could not show him to their friends or take him for a walk. He had to stay hidden in the house so that Pharaoh would not find out about him.

Yocheved fed the baby quietly. Miriam made her funny sounds in his ear so he would not cry. After three months, they couldn't hide him in the house any longer.

What would her mother do? Miriam watched as Yocheved began to make a little basket. She spread clay on the inside and sticky tar on the outside.

Then Yocheved lay her precious baby inside the basket, walked down to the river, and placed the basket into the water. It floated safely on the river like a little boat.

Miriam stood by and never took her eyes off that basket. What would happen to her baby brother?

Would he ever have the chance to lead all the Jews out of Mitzrayim someday?

Just then, Miriam saw Pharaoh's daughter, the Princess of Mitzrayim, coming down to the river with her many helpers.

"Look! A basket!" said Pharaoh's daughter. She stretched out her hand to reach it.

When the princess opened the basket, she was surprised to find a baby boy crying inside. "This must be a Jewish child," she said.

The princess knew that her father didn't want there to be any Jewish baby boys. But she was very kind, and she wanted to take care of this beautiful baby.

Miriam watched as Pharaoh's daughter
lifted the crying baby out of the
basket. It was hard for Miriam to see
someone else holding her brother.
She wanted to pick him up and cuddle
him herself.

The princess thought he was hungry,
but the baby wouldn't eat or drink
a thing. It was hard for Miriam to
see other people trying to feed her
brother.

Poor baby! He must really want his
own mother to feed him.

Suddenly, that little girl named Miriam had a great big wonderful idea. She came close to the princess who was holding the unhappy baby in her arms. Even though Pharaoh's daughter was so important and might not even listen, Miriam knew it was time to speak up.

"Would you like me to go and call a Jewish mother to feed that baby for you?"
"Oh, yes," answered the princess. "Please go!"

And so she did. Filled with happiness, little Miriam
ran faster than she'd ever run before. She ran all
the way home without stopping and called her very
own mother!
Yocheved was amazed that little Miriam could be
so clever.

Together, they went back to the princess.
Pharaoh's daughter looked at Yocheved and said,
"Take this baby I found, and I will pay you to feed
him for me."

Yocheved stretched out her arms. She took her
baby from the princess and hugged him close.
Joyfully, Miriam and her mother brought their
little baby home.

Since they were taking care of him for the princess, they didn't have to hide him. Now Miriam and her brother Aaron could show the baby to their friends and take him for a walk. Now their father, Amram, could hold his special son, and Yocheved could rock him to sleep.

Years later, that baby grew up to be Moshe Rabbeinu, who really did lead the Jews out of Mitzrayim. And it all started when little Miriam spoke up!

A NOTE TO PARENTS AND TEACHERS

This story is based on events described in the Book of Exodus, with additional details from the Midrash (Sh'mos Rabah) and Talmud Sotah.

Miriam was born in the year 2361 (1400 B.C.E.) During her childhood, the oppressive enslavement of the Jewish people under the Egyptians was in full force. In spite of the cruelty, the Jewish population grew in record numbers, and multiple births were the rule rather than the exception. Afraid of a strong Jewish nation joining with Egyptian enemies to overthrow him, Pharaoh tried to separate the husbands from their wives in order to diminish the huge number of Jewish babies being born. When that scheme was ineffective, he ordered the Jewish midwives, Yocheved and Miriam (Shifra and Pu'ah) to kill the Jewish male babies at birth. Finally, Pharaoh implemented the plan of throwing all male babies into the Nile. None of these wicked decrees succeeded. The righteous Jewish women continued to bear children, the courageous midwives defied Pharaoh's orders, and Hashem miraculously rescued the babies from the river, cared for them, and reunited them with their families.

Little Miriam was endowed with prophetic wisdom and knew that her prophecy of Moshe as the redeemer of the Jews would prove true. When her mother was forced to place the baby in a basket on the water, his very survival seemed precarious. Miriam didn't stand by merely to watch over him. With perfect faith, she waited to see exactly how Hashem's salvation would unfold. The Divine Intervention was unmistakable. After only fifteen minutes*, Pharaoh's daughter appeared and the baby was saved, paving the way for the end of slavery and oppression.

Eighty years later, when the Jews left Mitzrayim, Miriam's faith was just as strong and unshakable. After the splitting of the sea and the downfall of the Egyptians, Miriam took her tambourine and led all the women with their instruments in a song of thanksgiving. How did they happen to have these instruments on hand? Were drums, tambourines, and flutes on their list of priorities as they hastened from Egypt without time to bake proper bread? Absolutely. Even before the salvation was complete, Miriam and all the women prepared for the true redemption that would follow. The parallel to our own generation is clear. Now, more than ever, Jews need the certainty and the confidence to anticipate the Geulah that we were promised — days of peace, prosperity, and redemption for the entire world. We hope you and your "little greats" will aspire to Miriam's outstanding qualities as you enjoy her story over and over again.

D.L. Rosenfeld

* Tosafoth, Sotah 11a, s.v. Miriam.
  (Yalkut Me'am Loaz, Shemos 2:4)